Wild
Window
Art

This edition published in 2018
By SpiceBox™
12171 Horseshoe Way,
Richmond, BC
Canada V7A 4V4

First published in 2016

ISBN 10: 1-77132-420-1
ISBN 13: 978-1-77132-420-5

CEO & Publisher: Ben Lotfi
Editor: Ania Jaraczewski
Creative Director: Garett Chan
Art Director: Christine Covert
Design and Layout: Kimberly Ang
Production: James Badger, Mell D'Clute
Sourcing: Janny Lam, Carman Fung

For more SpiceBox products and
information, visit our website:
www.spiceboxbooks.com

Manufactured in China

7 9 10 8 6

Contents

Your Windows Will Never Be the Same!

Windows are meant to be ordinary, see-through surfaces, but in the right hands (yours!) they can be cool art canvases too. Be creative and splash some color onto plain, boring glass by making fun window clings that you can stick on and peel off to decorate stuff, create scenes and even make great gifts for your friends and family!

What You'll Need

Window paints

Inside your kit you'll find a few tubes of window paint. The black is for making outlines, which you can fill in with the colored paints. See pages 10–11 to see how it's done!

Designs to trace

The last few pages of this book are full of pictures that you can trace over. There are lots to choose from, so you can pick out the ones you like!

Plastic sheet

Always paint onto the plastic sheet included in your kit. The paint will stick to paper, so never squeeze paint directly onto the templates.

Seed beads, craft gems and glitter

See page 13 for some great ideas for making your window art extra awesome by adding some bling.

Toothpicks

Toothpicks will help you mix your colors to create cool effects like swirls and flames (see page 12). Keep a few handy!

Cotton swabs

Oops! If you make a mistake, don't panic. Just wipe away the paint while it's still wet using a cotton swab.

Surfaces

Once you've finished decorating all the windows in your home, you can take over everything else with your art! There are lots of surfaces you can cover:

Glass doors

Sliding glass doors are really just huge canvases waiting to be covered with art! See pages 26–27 for instructions on how to make your own window paint so you can create big murals.

Mirrors

Leave a fun message or picture for someone on the bathroom mirror for their birthday, or just to say hi!

Car windows

Make Mother's Day or Father's Day special by leaving a window art surprise on their car window.

Drinking glasses

Personalize a water glass for everyone in your family by writing out their names or making other fun little window art creations!

How to create Window Art

Making glass art is easy! The paints in your kit dry to create cool window clings that you can peel off and stick onto any glass surface.

1. Pick a template you'd like to trace and put the plastic sheet over top of it.

2. Use the black paint to make your outline to keep all your other colors in the right place! Only black works for outlines.

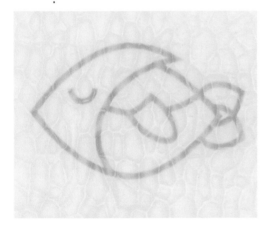

3. Hold the bottle just above the plastic and press the sides gently so that the paint comes out smoothly.

4. Let the black dry a bit before adding other colors.

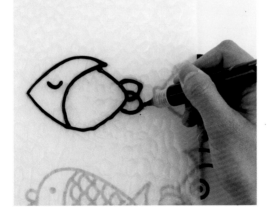

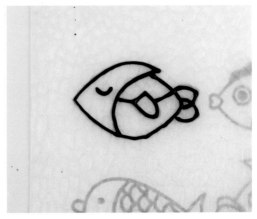

5. Fill in the spaces between the black lines with whatever colors you want!

6. Leave the paint to dry for 24 hours.

7. Carefully peel your window art off the plastic sheet. Lift up any finicky corners first. Make sure it doesn't fold over and stick to itself!

8. Stick your design onto a glass surface like a window or mirror. Tada!

All Mixed Up

Your black outlines will keep your colors apart, but if you want you can also make some cool effects by swirling different colors together. Here's how to mix colors like a pro:

1. Make your black outline as usual.

2. Pick out 2 colors. Put a little bit of one color in the area you want to fill.

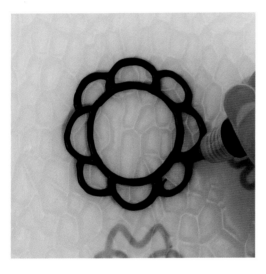

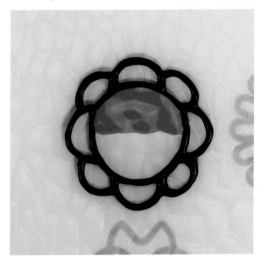

3. Squeeze in a little bit of the second color beside it.

4. Take a toothpick and swirl the two colors together until you get the look you want. You can make stripes, swirls, flames...experiment!

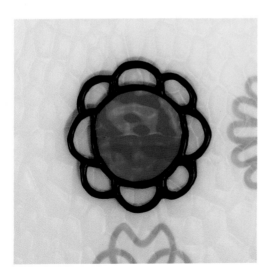

Embellishing Your Window Art

There are lots of ways to make your window art more exciting. Small, shiny shimmery things will stick to window paint, so you can bling out your art!

Glitter it up!

For some added sparkle, sprinkle a bit of loose glitter over top of your paint while it's still wet.

Bling it out

While the paint is still wet, add small, flat craft gems and sequins to make your art glitzy and glamorous.

Beadazzle it

Tiny seed beads will easily stick to your window paint. Gently press them into your picture while the paint is still wet.

Now sit back and watch the sun sparkle through your window art!

Hints & Tips

Stick to glass

It might seem like fun to put your window clings on walls, furniture or plastic surfaces, but this paint is made for glass only. It may permanently stick to anything else!

Don't mess with window art

Paint doesn't always go where you want it to! Wear old clothes that won't mind some extra color, and cover your work surface with newspaper.

14

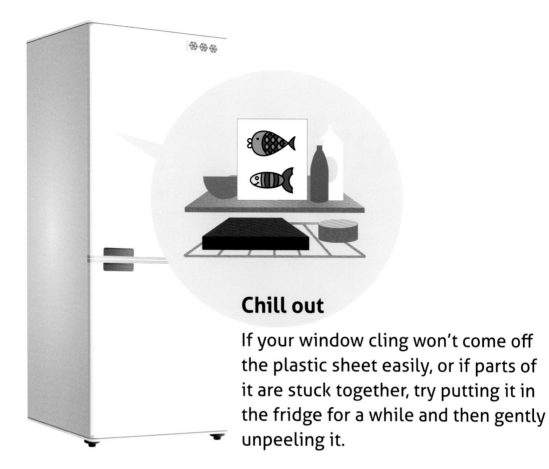

Chill out

If your window cling won't come off the plastic sheet easily, or if parts of it are stuck together, try putting it in the fridge for a while and then gently unpeeling it.

Storing your art

You can store your window clings by carefully sliding them into plastic sheet protectors. Save your holiday-themed window clings for next year!

Window Chalk Markers

Besides window paints, you can also use a chalk marker to create cool window art. Here are some fun ideas for using chalk markers:

Adding details

After you stick your window clings to the glass, you can use a chalk marker to add little details. For example, you can create some colorful balloons with your paints, then draw in the strings with your marker. Or draw a spiderweb with the marker and stick a window cling spider in the middle for a Halloween decoration. What else can you think of?

Tracing

You can also trace the templates in your book right onto the glass with your marker. Just photocopy a page from your book and tape it to the other side of the glass, then trace over the lines with your marker.

Writing messages

If you don't have time to make window cling letters, you can just use the marker to jot down a quick message for someone. Guaranteed to make their day!

Make a Scene!

If you look at the templates, you'll see that a lot of the designs go together, like the farm animals or the dinosaurs. Create a bunch of window clings in the same set and arrange them on your window in a fun scene! Here are some ideas:

Aquarium
Garden
Safari
Jungle
Outer space
Farm

Wonderful Window Words

You can use the letter templates at the back of the book to create colorful labels and messages. Or you can come up with your own lettering styles using the paints or a chalk pen. Here are some ideas that you can try:

Mirror message

Make someone a sweet message like "Happy Birthday," "Happy Mother's Day" or "Good Luck!" Stick it on their bedroom window or on the bathroom mirror. What a great way to let someone know you're thinking of them!

Storage jars

Make some flashy DIY storage containers out of empty jars. Take a clean, empty jar and use your window paints to make a label like "paints" or "markers."

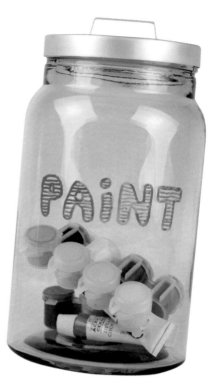

Water bottle

Make your own personalized water bottle! Take a glass water bottle and stick your name or initials on it.

Flowers for you

Take the idea of a special message one step further and put a bouquet of flowers into a glass vase decorated with your words.

Frames and Borders

You can use your paints to make a cool border for a window or a mirror. Or look in the back of the book for some templates that you can trace to make photo frames.

Borders

Paint some repeating pictures or shapes all around the outside edges of a window or mirror to give it a cool border. Here are some ideas:

• flowers (you can trace the
  ones in the book)

• simple shapes like stars and circles

• hearts for Valentine's Day

• spiderwebs in the corners
  for Halloween

• holly and berries for Christmas

Picture it

Find the frame templates in the book and create colorful photo frames. Just trace over the design and let it dry. Cut a photo to a size that is just bigger than the opening in the frame, hold the photo against the glass and stick the frame over it. Voilà!

Warning: Window paint might stain your photos. Use a photo that you don't mind getting marks on, or make a copy.

WOW

Be creative!

We've given you lots of templates that you can trace over to make your window art, but it's also fun to be creative and come up with your own unique pictures!

Draw it!

Sketch out a picture of something that you like, then place it under the plastic sheet. When you paint it, make sure to trace over your outline with the black paint and then fill in all the blank spaces with colored paints.

Trace a photo

You can even trace over a photo of a person or a pet! Just make a rough outline of their features and ignore the little details when you make your sketch. Then fill in the shapes with your colored paints.

Make Your own Window Paint

If you run out of paint from your kit, there's an easy way to make your own!

You will need:

- liquid food coloring
- liquid dish soap
- paintbrush
- small, disposable containers
- clear plastic sheet
- craft glue that dries clear

1. Pour a small amount of glue (about 2 tablespoons) into a container. You will need a separate container for each color you make.

2. Mix some food coloring, drop by drop, until you get the color you want. Repeat for the other colors.

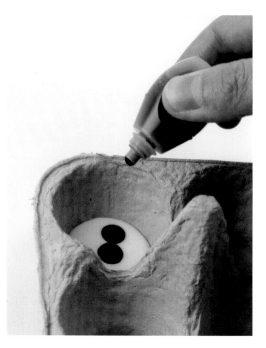

3. Add a couple of drops of dish soap into each of your colors.

4. Mix your paint until the color is even. Pick a template from the book, or create your own, and place the plastic sheet over it.

5. Use the paintbrush to spread a nice, thick layer of paint over your design.

6. Let your picture dry for 24 hours, then you can peel it off the sheet and...voilà! You have window art!

Templates

Check out pages 10–11 to see how to create your own wonderful window art using the fun designs on these pages!

1 2 3 4
5 6 7 8
9 0 & ?
! @ #

1 2 3 4 5
6 7 8 9 0
& ? ! @ #

48